Kingdom Hearts Volumes 1 & 2
Adapted by
Shiro Amano

Associate Editors – Alexis Kirsch and Peter Ahlstrom
Copy Editors – Eric Althoff and Seraphina Wong
Retouch and Lettering – Adriana Rivera and Joe Macasocol, Jr.
Production Artists – Chris Anderson and Ana Lopez
Cover Layout – Gary Shum

Editor - Bryce P. Coleman
Digital Imaging Manager - Chris Buford
Pre-Production Supervisor - Erika Terriquez
Production Manager - Elisabeth Brizzi
Managing Editor - Vy Nguyen
Creative Director - Anne Marie Horne
Editor-in-Chief - Rob Tokar
Publisher - Mike Kiley
President and C.O.O. - John Parker
C.E.O. and Chief Creative Officer - Stuart Levy

A  Manga

TOKYOPOP Inc.
5900 Wilshire Blvd. Suite 2000
Los Angeles, CA 90036

E-mail: info@TOKYOPOP.com
Come visit us online at www.TOKYOPOP.com

ISBN: 978-1-4278-1269-8

First TOKYOPOP printing: January 2008
10 9 8 7 6 5 4 3 2 1
Printed in the USA

Disney ｜ SQUARESOFT

Volume 1

Adapted by
Shiro Amano

HAMBURG // LONDON // LOS ANGELES // TOKYO

KINGDOM HEARTS: VOLUME 1
TABLE OF CONTENTS

Long ago, the world was united and filled with warm light.

People loved the light, and eventually began fighting over it.

Then, darkness found its way into people's hearts.

Darkness consumed the hearts and light of the people, and in a flash, it spread... The world disappeared into the darkness.

But a glimmer of light remained in the hearts of children...

Children gathered their glimmers of light and re-created the world.

The re-created world, however, was no longer united... It was divided into several smaller worlds.

Because the true light was still hidden deep within the darkness...

WHO...ARE YOU?

WHERE DID YOU COME FROM...?

Episode 1
Calling

IF KAIRI HADN'T COME TO THIS ISLAND...

...WE NEVER WOULD'VE KNOWN THAT THERE IS ANOTHER WORLD OUT THERE.

WE WOULD'VE LIVED OUR ENTIRE LIVES ON THIS ISLAND...

HEY, GUYS...

SAILORS USED TO WEAR THESE AND PRAY FOR A SAFE VOYAGE...

...IN HOPES OF RETURNING SAFELY HOME FROM THEIR JOURNEYS.

A THALASSA SHELL LUCKY CHARM!

CHECK THIS OUT!

THERE'S NOTHING TO WORRY ABOUT!

11

So little time...

The door is still shut...

Take it easy.

Don't be scared.

MY GOODNESS!!

I'M NOT SURE WHY, BUT THE STARS HAVE BEEN BLINKING OUT...ONE BY ONE.

HATE TO LEAVE YOU, BUT I HAVE TO CHECK INTO THIS...

......

PAOPU FRUIT...

MAN...

WHAT A FAIRY TALE!

AS THE KING, I HAVE A FAVOR TO ASK YOU AND GOOFY...

G'NIGHT!

THERE'S SOMEONE OUT THERE WITH A KEY-- THE KEY TO OUR SURVIVAL. I NEED YOU AND GOOFY TO FIND HIM AND STICK WITH HIM! GOT IT?

Episode 2
Invader

SORA?

ド ド ゛...

WHERE ARE YOU?

ARGH!

WE HAVE TO GET READY FOR TOMORROW'S DEPARTURE...

THIS IS RIKU'S AND MY SECRET PLACE!

NO ONE'S SUPPOSED TO COME IN HERE!

KAIRI, I'LL LET YOU IN BECAUSE YOU'RE SPECIAL!

WOW, THAT'S COOL!

BEFORE WE DEPART...

THE WORLD HAS BEEN CONNECTED...

Episode 3
Light in the Hand

THERE'S NOTHING...

IT'S PITCH DARK...

!?

!

Episode 4
Giant Shadow

DON'T BE AFRAID.

WHAT ON EARTH IS GOING ON?!

I GUESS I HAVE NO CHOICE...

 AREN'T YOU A LITTLE TOO BIG?

WHEN YOU ENCOUNTER A GIANT ENEMY, AIM FOR THE EYE.

NO ONE CAN TRAIN ONE'S EYES...

WHAT SHOULD I DO???

Excerpt from "Battle with the Bengal Tiger" written by boxer, Shihoro Okada.

YAA!!

WHO?

YOUR FACE IS WIDE OPEN!

Episode 5
Cast Ashore

WHAT?!!

WHAT'S GOING ON?

A... DOG?!

WAIT A MINUTE...

WHERE AM I?

I WAS SUCKED IN WITH THAT GIANT...

BUT, WHERE IS THIS PLACE?!

YOU FINALLY ARRIVED...

THE HOLDER OF THE KEY.

......

I GUESS YOU WOULDN'T KNOW, HUH?

ポッポッ

HEY, WAIT!

ワワッ

HERE WE GO AGAIN...

Episode 6
"Traverse Town"

YOU'RE BAD FOR BUSINESS, CREEPS!

THERE WE GO.

HEY KID, YOU NEW AROUND HERE?

I'M NOT A KID! AND THE NAME'S SORA.

ALL RIGHT, ALL RIGHT. NICE TO MEET YOU, SORA.

THE HEARTLESS ARE MONSTERS WHO EAT PEOPLE'S HEARTS.

WHERE'D YOU COME FROM?

HAVEN'T SEEN THEM IN THIS PART OF TOWN FOR A WHILE...

EAT THAT AND RECHARGE YOURSELF.

ALTHOUGH IT'S A LEFTOVER.

COME BACK ANY TIME YOU NEED SOME HELP!

HALF EATEN

UH, GRAMPS...

DON'T CALL ME GRAMPS!

THE NAME'S CID!

THANKS, GRAMPS!

THEY'LL KEEP COMING AFTER YOU...

...AS LONG AS YOU WIELD THE KEYBLADE.

ACCESSORY

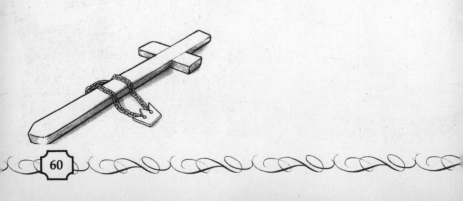

Episode 7
The Man Named Leon

OOH...

KAIRI? WHO'S THAT?

MY NAME IS YUFFIE!

I THINK YOU OVERDID IT, SQUALL.

KAIRI...?!

THAT'S LEON!

LEEEOOON!

WHERE ARE YOU?!

I WONDER WHERE HE IS...

THIS TOWN IS TOO HUGE!

IF WE DON'T HURRY, WE'LL NEVER FIND THE KEY!

UH-YUH!

THE KEYBLADE YOU HAVE...

THAT'S WHAT THE HEARTLESS ARE LOOKING FOR.

I CONCEALED YOUR HEART SO THEY WOULDN'T FIND YOU.

HEY, WAIT A MINUTE.

MAKE SENSE! WHAT'S GOING ON HERE?

DARN, THEY'RE ALREADY HERE...

LEON!

YUFFIE, GO!

I'LL EXPLAIN LATER-- JUST FOLLOW ME!

WHAT? HEY!

WOW! HE'S PRETTY GOOD.

YOU WERE LOOKING FOR ME...?

71

HEY, WHY NOT JOIN US?! WE CAN GO TO THE OTHER WORLDS IN OUR SHIP!

......

RIKU AND KAIRI...?

WE'LL FIND THEM, TOO!

REALLY?

WHO KNOWS!

BUT WE NEED HIM TO FIND THE KING!

THEY, TOO, HAVE BEEN SEEKING THE WIELDER OF THE KEYBLADE.

SORA, GO WITH THEM.

ESPECIALLY IF YOU WANT TO FIND YOUR FRIENDS.

......

OKAY...

Episode 8
Conspiracy

THAT LITTLE
SQUIRT TOOK
DOWN THE GIANT
HEARTLESS!

SUCH IS THE POWER
OF THE KEYBLADE.
THE CHILD'S STRENGTH
IS NOT HIS OWN.

TURN HIM INTO A
HEARTLESS. THAT WILL
SETTLE THINGS QUICK
ENOUGH.

WE GOTTA PROTECT THE WORLD BORDER!

GAH! THE "ORDER"!

THE ORDER OF WORLDS ARE BEING DISRUPTED...

...DUE TO THE HEARTLESS.

GOT IT.

WHAT ARE THEY, ANYWAY?

HEARTLESS... THOSE WITHOUT HEARTS.

A RESEARCHER NAMED ANSEM FILED A REPORT ON THE HEARTLESS.

I THINK IT MIGHT HELP SOLVE THE MYSTERY, BUT...

...THE REPORT IS SCATTERED EVERYWHERE, AND WE CAN'T FIND IT ALL.

WHAT DO YOU MEAN, "EVERYWHERE"?

GAWRSH! THAT MEANS THE KING--

RIGHT.

I MEAN, DIFFERENT WORLDS!

HE MIGHT HAVE GONE LOOKING FOR THAT REPORT!

THEY FEED OFF THE DARKNESS IN PEOPLE'S HEARTS.

WATCH YOUSELF.

THERE IS DARKNESS IN EVERY HEART.

Episode 9
Departure

Inside the Gummi Ship

COCK PIT

WOW!

WELCOME TO OUR GUMMI SHIP!

PRETTY SPACIOUS... UH-YUP!

WOW, LOOK AT THIS!!

CHECK THIS OUT! COOL!

THAT'S ENOUGH!!!

WILL YOU STOP TOUCHING EVERYTHING YOU SEE?!

WHA—?

HUH?

DOWN HERE!!

WE'RE TRYING TO KEEP THIS PLACE CLEAN!

DON'T MAKE A MESS, OKAY?

THOSE ARE CHIP 'N' DALE.

HEY! DON'T CALL US "THOSE"!

THEY'RE THE MECHANICS OF THE GUMMI SHIP.

NICE TO MEET YOU!

TAKE OFF YOUR SHOES WHEN YOU ENTER THE COCKPIT!

OKAY!

Episode 10
Kangaroo Court

WOW!

THE OUTSIDE WORLD IS SO MYSTERIOUS!!

COOL!

I THINK THIS IS A LITTLE TOO MYSTERIOUS...

OKAY.

LET'S GO...

WE'RE REALLY SMALL!

HEY, LET US THROUGH.

ZZZZ...

HEY, WAKE UP!

SORA, THIS WAY!

I THINK WE CAN GET THROUGH THIS HOLE.

OH BROTHER...

PHEW!

THE COURT IS NOW IN SESSION!

Episode 11
Find the Evidence!

JUST YOU WAIT! WE'LL FIND THE TRUE CRIMINAL!

THE *CHESHIRE CAT* I MET IN THE WOODS MAY KNOW SOMETHING.

BUT BE CAREFUL--

BUT WHERE CAN WE FIND EVIDENCE?

GET GOING!

YOU MAY NOT SPEAK WITH THE DEFENDANT!

LET'S TELL THE QUEEN THAT THE HEARTLESS DID IT.

WE'RE ALREADY DEEPLY INTERFERING WITH THIS WORLD ANYWAY.

NO!!

EVERY PERSON SHOULD KEEP LIVING ONLY IN THEIR OWN WORLD.

REALLY?

IT'LL JUST CAUSE CONFUSION. THAT'S WHY WE HAVE TO KEEP IT A SECRET.

WELL, THAT MAY OR MAY NOT BE TRUE.

THE CHESHIRE CAT KNOWS EVERYTHING.

ALL YOU HAVE TO DO IS AVOID GETTING CONFUSED.

THE CHESHIRE CAT!

HERE YOU GO.

!

THE EVIDENCE YOU SEEK IS IN THAT BOX.

...OR IS IT?

TO TRUST, OR NOT TO TRUST?

I TRUST YOU'LL DECIDE.

HIN...

HE'S GONE!

WHAT A CREEPY GUY...

WHAT'S IN HERE?

!!

IT'S A HEARTLESS!

STOP!!

?!!

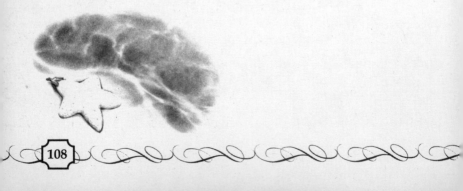

Episode 12
Helping Hand

THAT QUEEN IS CRAZY!

THE HEARTLESS PROBABLY TOOK ALICE...

I THOUGHT THE HEARTLESS ONLY ATTACKED PEOPLE ON THE SPOT.

...BUT SOMETHING MAY BE MANIPULATING THE HEARTLESS.

I'M NOT SURE...

SOMETHING REALLY EVIL...

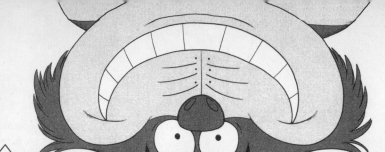

AHHH!!

MIGHT YOU BE LOOKING FOR ALICE?

YEAH! DID YOU SEE HER?

NO.

THEN WHAT DO YOU WANT?!

WELL, I KNOW WHERE THE SHADOW IS.

THIS WAY? THAT WAY?

WHERE...?

DOES IT MATTER?

DID YOU KNOW THAT...

...WHEN YOU TURN ON THE LIGHT, A SHADOW IS MADE?

ARE YOU PREPARED FOR THE WORST?

IF YOU'RE NOT... THAT'S TOO BAD!

YOU...

YOU TRICKED US!!!

TRICKED YOU? NOTHING OF THE SORT!

THE CHESHIRE CAT IS ALWAYS HERE TO HELP THE WEAK.

HOT! HOT!

WHOA!!

DONALD!

?!

SORA?!

DID YOU JUST DO THAT?

THE WIELDER OF THE KEYBLADE...

...SHOULD BE ABLE TO USE A LITTLE MAGIC, RIGHT?

PUT ME OUT, TOO!

Episode 13
Keyhole

LET ME SLEEP IN PEACE...

WHAT... WAS THAT?

IT SOUNDED LIKE SOMETHING CLOSED WITH A *CLICK.*

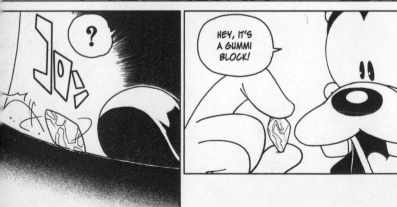

?

HEY, IT'S A GUMMI BLOCK!

UH, BUT THIS GUMMI AIN'T LIKE OTHERS, NO SIR!

GIVE IT HERE.

YOU'RE RIGHT. I'VE NEVER SEEN THIS KIND OF GUMMI BLOCK BEFORE.

GUMMI BLOCK?

YEAH, THEY'RE USED AS COMPONENTS FOR OUR GUMMI SHIP.

パチ パチ

SPLENDID! YOU'RE QUITE THE HERO.

!

REALLY QUITE EXCELLENT! YOUR POWER HAS BLOSSOMED!

I CAN'T WAIT TO SEE WHAT YOU'LL DO NEXT!

CHESHIRE CAT...

...WHO ARE YOU?

THAT DARN CAT...

IT NEEDS TO SHUT ITS BIG MOUTH!

WE SHOULD HAVE FINISHED HIM OFF WHEN HE TURNED DOWN OUR OFFER.

TOO LATE FOR THAT.

EVEN IF WE LET HIM LIVE, HE CAN'T DO US MUCH HARM.

BUT THE BOY IS A PROBLEM.

HE FOUND ONE OF THE KEYHOLES.

WE NEED TO TAKE CARE OF THIS RIGHT AWAY--

THERE'S NO NEED TO RUSH.

IT WILL TAKE HIM AGES TO FIND THE OTHERS.

BESIDES...

!

THE PIECES ARE ALL FALLING INTO PLACE IN OUR FAVOR!

The End of Kingdom Hearts volume 1

Sora

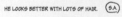

HE LOOKS BETTER WITH LOTS OF HAIR. S.A.

Kairi

Riku

Shadows

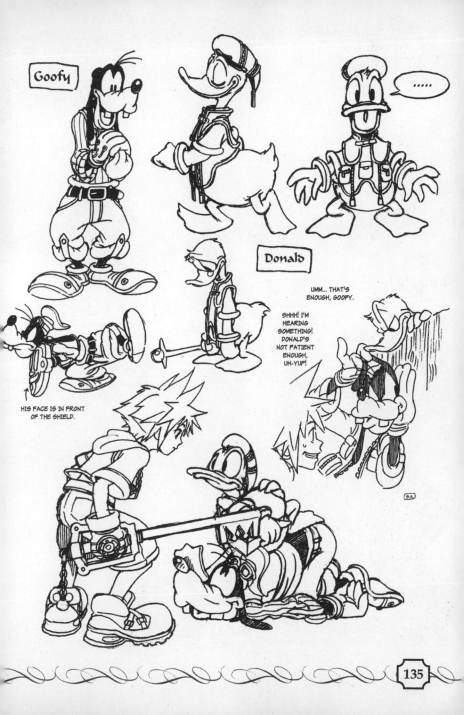

DISNEY | SQUARESOFT

KINGDOM HEARTS

Volume 2

Adapted by
Shiro Amano

TOKYOPOP®

HAMBURG // LONDON // LOS ANGELES // TOKYO

KINGDOM HEARTS: VOLUME 2 TABLE OF CONTENTS

Episode 14
Sentimental Journey

ALL RIGHT, DONALD! WHAT'S OUR NEXT COURSE?

I WANNA BE PILOT!

HEY! STOP IT!

OKAY, TALK TO YOU LATER, CID.

143

I CAN'T BELIEVE YOU RAMMED US INTO A METEOR!

プシニ

UM, THAT'S WHY WE'RE BACK...

......

THAT'S THE LAST TIME I'M LETTING YOU FLY OUR SHIP!!

I... SEE...

WE ALSO WANT TO ASK LEON SOME THINGS.

LEON'S PROBABLY IN THE BASEMENT. HE TRAINS THERE ALL THE TIME.

I DIDN'T KNOW THERE WAS A PLACE LIKE THIS UNDERGROUND...

SO...

YOU FOUND THE KEYHOLE...

Episode 15
The Chosen One

SO, YOU FOUND THE KEYHOLE...

YEAH.

THE KEYBLADE GLOWED...

...AND LOCKED IT AUTOMATICALLY.

ACCORDING TO ANSEM'S REPORT...

...EACH WORLD AMONG THE STARS...

...HAS A KEYHOLE THAT LEADS TO THE HEART OF THAT WORLD.

THE HEART OF THE WORLD?

THAT'S WHY THE KEYHOLES MUST BE LOCKED...

...USING THIS KEYBLADE.

YOU'RE THE ONLY ONE WHO CAN DO IT, SORA.

BESIDES, SEEING OTHER WORLDS WOULD PROBABLY SERVE YOU WELL.

SO THAT'S WHY--

B-BUT I'M JUST A--

DON'T WORRY.

YOU CAN DO IT...

...SORA.

THIS IS AERITH.

SHE'S A FRIEND OF OURS.

WOULD YOU LIKE SOME LEMONADE?

THANKS.

I ASKED CID TO FIX THE GUMMI SHIP.

REALLY?

I'LL PASS...

OH YEAH...

I FOUND THIS GUMMI BLOCK THAT'S DIFFERENT FROM THE OTHERS. ANY IDEA WHAT IT'S FOR?

ASK CID. HE SHOULD KNOW.

GREAT... THANKS.

COME ON, DONALD, GOOFY. LET'S GO!

THOUGH WHILE I'M WORKING ON THAT...

...I'VE GOT SOMETHING I NEED *YOU* DO TO FOR *ME*.

HUUUH?!

HAVEN'T YOU HEARD OF "GIVE AND TAKE"?

DON'T MAKE ME ANGRY!

GOTCHA!!

I NEED YOU TO DELIVER THIS BOOK.

WHAT IS IT?

A LOVE DIARY?

NO!!

IT GOES TO THE OLD HOUSE PAST THE THIRD DISTRICT.

YOU CAN'T MISS IT.

Episode 16
Wizard's House

EXCUSE ME!

ANYBODY HOME?

HEY...

THE DOOR'S OPEN.

WOW.

PHEW!

WELL, WELL... YOU'VE ARRIVED SOONER THAN I EXPECTED.

WHAT WAS THAT?

SO CID REPAIRED THE BOOK, DID HE? EXCELLENT!

WHAT A TERRIBLE LANDING... ≥COUGH COUGH≤

MY NAME IS MERLIN. AS YOU CAN SEE, I AM A SORCERER.

YOUR KING HAS REQUESTED THAT I HELP YOU OUT.

THE KING?! WHERE IS HE?

WELL, NOW, LET ME SEE... THAT'S A GOOD QUESTION.

BUT ONE THING IS FOR CERTAIN--

SWIRL SWIRL

YOUR KING IS TRYING TO BRING PEACE BACK TO ALL THE WORLDS.

UH-YUH!

HE ASKED ME TO TRAIN YOU IN THE ART OF MAGIC.

ME?

YOU'RE STILL USING THE POWER OF THE KEYBLADE INSTINCTIVELY.

YOU MUST LEARN TO CONTROL THIS POWER.

ESPECIALLY SORA.

NEVER FORGET WHAT I'VE TOLD YOU.

COME BACK ANYTIME YOU NEED ADVICE.

ALL RIGHT?

AND ONE MORE THING...

IF YOU FIND ANY MISSING PAGES FROM THIS BOOK, PLEASE HANG ON TO THEM.

A BOOK HAS A WORLD OF ITS OWN, AND IT WOULD BE SAD IF THE WORLD WERE INCOMPLETE.

IT LOOKS LIKE WE HAVE MORE THINGS TO FIND.

LET'S TAKE IT ONE STEP AT A TIME.

YEAH, ONE STEP AT A TIME!

SHOOT!

?!

HEY, WAKE UP, SORA!

NO WAY!!

Episode 17
Reunion

IT TOOK FOREVER TO FIND YOU, SORA.

RIKU!!

HEY! CUT THAT OUT!

WOW! YOU'RE FOR REAL, RIKU!

...WAIT A SECOND-- WHERE'S KAIRI?

ISN'T SHE WITH YOU? ...WELL, DON'T WORRY.

WE'RE FINALLY FREE TO GO ANYWHERE WE WANT.

BUMMER...

I'M SURE SHE'S MADE IT OFF THE ISLAND, TOO.

HEY, I'LL BET SHE'S LOOKING FOR US HERE IN THE OUTER WORLD RIGHT NOW.

WE'LL ALL BE TOGETHER AGAIN SOON. DON'T WORRY.

HISS...

JUST LEAVE EVERYTHING TO ME.

I KNOW THIS--

SO, THIS IS CALLED A **KEYBLADE?**

HUH?!

HEY! GIVE IT BACK!

HMM...

CATCH.

POOF!

!

HOW DID HE DO THAT?

SORA CAN'T EVEN DO THAT!

HUH?

WELL...

OKAY! SO, YOU'RE COMING WITH US, RIGHT?

WE'VE GOT THIS AWESOME SHIP!

WAIT 'TIL YOU SEE IT!

SORA! YOU CAN'T JUST DECIDE THINGS ON YOUR OWN!

OH, COME ON! HE'S MY FRIEND!

I'M SURE RIKU WANTS TO JOIN US.

RIGHT, RIKU?

HEY...

RIKU!

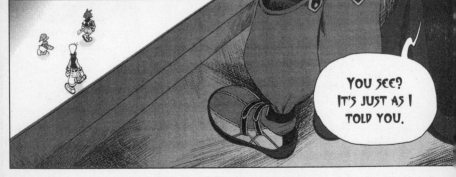

YOU SEE? IT'S JUST AS I TOLD YOU.

WHILE YOU TOILED AWAY TRYING TO FIND YOUR DEAR FRIEND, HE SIMPLY REPLACED YOU WITH SOME NEW COMPANIONS.

EVIDENTLY, HE VALUES THEM FAR MORE THAN HE DOES YOU, NOW.

YOU'RE BETTER OFF WITHOUT THAT WRETCHED BOY.

NOW, THINK NO MORE OF HIM AND COME WITH ME.

I'LL HELP YOU FIND WHAT YOU'RE SEARCHING FOR...

Episode 18
Maleficent

WHERE DID HE GO?!

I STILL HAD SO MUCH TO ASK HIM!

RIKU!

SORA...

OH WELL.

AT LEAST HE'S OKAY!

WHO KNOWS? MAYBE WE'LL RUN INTO KAIRI SOON, TOO.

HUH? WHAT'S WRONG, DONALD?

YOUR MOODS SURE CHANGE QUICKLY...

HEY!

A-HYUCK?

ARE YOU GUYS DONE WITH YOUR ERRAND?

COME THIS WAY.

DRESS & SUIT

WE'RE GOING TO HAVE A STRATEGY MEETING IN OUR SECRET HIDEOUT.

YOO-HOO, YUFFIE HAS ARRIVED!

OOPS...

ずもーーん...

IS IT GLOOMY IN HERE, OR WHAT?

YOU GUYS EVER HEAR OF MALEFICENT? I HEAR SHE'S IN TOWN.

WHA?!

173

? MALE-WHO?

SHE'S BEEN USING THE HEARTLESS FOR YEARS. WE LOST OUR WORLD, THANKS TO HER.

A WITCH, MAN!

SHE'S A WITCH!

ONE DAY, A SWARM OF HEARTLESS TOOK OVER OUR WORLD! THAT WAS NINE YEARS AGO.

THAT'S WHY I GOT OUT OF THAT MESS AND CAME HERE WITH THESE GUYS.

THAT'S AWFUL!

I DIDN'T KNOW THAT...

MALEFICENT IS PROBABLY LOOKING FOR ANSEM'S RESEARCH.

HE WAS OUR RULER, AND HE DEDICATED HIS LIFE TO STUDYING THE HEARTLESS.

HIS REPORT SHOULD TELL US HOW TO GET RID OF THEM.

BUT IT GOT SCATTERED WHEN OUR WORLD WAS DESTROYED.

I'M SURE MALEFICENT'S ALREADY GOT MOST OF THE PAGES.

THEN LET'S DO IT!

LET'S FIND THE REST OF THE PAGES!

AND STOP THE WITCH'S PLAN!

OKAY ?!

I FIXED THE SHIP AND INSTALLED THAT NEW NAVIGATION GUMMI!

GOOD LUCK, BOYS!

...

WE'RE NOT JUST BEING... *USED*, ARE WE?

SORA?

I WAS THINKING...

MAYBE RIKU'S MAD AT ME...

BUT WHY WOULD THAT BE?

HE ACTUALLY *WAS* WORRIED!

LOOK! THAT'S OUR NEXT DESTINATION.

HUFF...

PUFF...

HUFF...

Episode 19
Agrabah

AND I'M CERTAIN THAT THE HEARTLESS WILL LOCATE THIS CITY'S KEYHOLE SOON ENOUGH.

THEY HAD BETTER.

AND WHAT ABOUT THE PRINCESS?

BAD NEWS, JAFAR! JASMINE'S GONE!

DISAPPEARED LIKE MAGIC!

HMPH.

SHE'S CRAFTY, THAT ONE.

AGRABAH IS FULL OF HOLES...

...FOR RATS TO HIDE IN.

YOU BETTER SUCCEED...

...IN FINDING THE PRINCESS. WE NEED HER.

OF COURSE...

HMPH...

YOUR CONCERN IS TOUCHING, BUT HARDLY NECESSARY.

......

THANK YOU, ABU.

OOH OOH!

BUT I CAN'T BELIEVE THAT AGRABAH WAS TAKEN OVER BY JAFAR.

OH NO...

IT LOOKS LIKE WE'RE SAFE NOW.

I HOPE ALADDIN IS ALL RIGHT!

!!!

SCREE!!

JASMINE HAS SOFT BLACK HAIR AND BEAUTIFUL SPARKLING EYES.

I'M CRAZY ABOUT HER...

BUT SHE'S A PRINCESS, AND I'M...

AW, SHE COULD NEVER FALL FOR A GUY LIKE ME.

ALADDIN, THAT'S NOT TRUE!

RIGHT, EVERYONE?

YEAH!

A-HYUCK!

STICK YOUR NECK OUT!

THAT'S RIGHT!

BESIDES, YOU'RE HANDSOME!

OH, STOP THAT...YOU'RE EMBARRASSING ME...

JUST HELP US ALREADY!!

OOPS, I ALMOST FORGOT!

HOLD ON A SECOND...

RUB RUB

COME ON OUT, GENIE!

Episode 20
The Genie of the Lamp

THANKS. YOU'RE A LIFESAVER.

CARAVANS HARDLY EVER PASS THROUGH HERE.

GOOD THING I HAPPENED TO PASS BY.

WHAT ARE YOU GUYS DOING HERE, ANYWAY?

A-HYUCK!

WE JUMPED OFF OUR GUMMI SHIP AND GOT CAUGHT IN THE QUICKS--

ALADDIN, WHAT'RE *YOU* DOING OUT HERE?

IN THIS DESERT...

ME?

HUNTING LEGENDARY TREASURE.

JUST PAID A VISIT TO THE CAVE OF WONDERS.

THAT'S WHERE I FOUND THIS LAMP!

WAIT A MINUTE!

HUH?

I THINK I'LL PUT THAT ON HOLD UNTIL WE REACH AGRABAH.

THEN I WANT TO BECOME A PRINCE...

...SO THAT I CAN PROPOSE TO JASMINE...

WAY TO GO, ALADDIN!

COME ON, LAY OFF...

NO PROBLEM!

THAT'LL GIVE ME MORE TIME TO ENJOY THE FRESH AIR!

BREATHE IN, BREATHE OUT...

GUESS YOU DON'T GET OUT MUCH, HUH?

COMES WITH THE JOB.

PHENO-MENAL COSMIC POWERS!

ITTY-BITTY LIVING SPACE.

IT'S ALWAYS THREE WISHES, THEN BACK TO MY PORTABLE PRISON!

I'M LUCKY TO SEE THE LIGHT OF DAY EVERY CENTURY OR TWO...

Episode 21
Devil's Grin

ARE YOU GUYS GOING TO AGRABAH, TOO?

IT'S A LITTLE FAR FROM HERE, BUT...

OH!

IF YOU ASK GENIE, IT'LL ONLY TAKE A MINUTE!

UM, I DON'T THINK THAT'S A VERY SMART THING TO USE YOUR WISH ON, ALADDIN...

THINK BEFORE YOU WISH...

HUH?

SKIRREEHEEN! (ALADDIN!)

MMF...

MMMFF!

PRINCESS JASMINE, MY APOLOGIES FOR TREATING YOU LIKE THIS.

UMPH!!!

HEY, JAFAR, DO YOU THINK THAT STREET RAT WILL COME TO RESCUE JASMINE?

OF COURSE HE'LL COME...

...WITH THAT LAMP IN HIS HAND.

THAT'S WHY WE SET THAT MONKEY LOOSE.

JAFAR, YOU'RE SO EVIL.

ALADDIN, IT'S A TRAP! PLEASE STAY AWAY...

YOUR EVILDOING STOPS HERE!

WHERE'S JASMINE?!

HEY... THAT'S SUPPOSED TO BE *MY* LINE...

OOPS...

PTHI.

TOO LATE.

ALADDIN! STAY AWAY!

IT'S A TRAP!

Episode 22
Endless Greed

DON'T FLINCH, GOOFY!

GAWRSH!

WHOA!!

HERE...

ENJOY YOUR STAY IN THIS JAR, MY DEAR, ANNOYING PRINCESS.

ALADDIN!

......!!

POP POP

MY FIRST WISH...

...GENIE.

SHOW ME THE **KEYHOLE!**

AYE AYE, SIR!

RUB-A-DUB-DUB THE LAMP AND HAVE YOUR DEAREST WISHES GRANTED!

THIS IS YOUR **SECOND** WISH! AND DON'T TRY TO TELL ME THAT I'M...

...WRONG...

OOPS... WRONG GUY...

VFFF

HUFF

HUFF

LET'S HURRY!

ABU! WHAT ARE YOU DOING?!

THIS WAY.

SORA?!

IT SEEMS STRANGE...

...BUT THE KEYBLADE IS TELLING ME TO GO *THIS* WAY!

ズ… ズン…

?!

WHAT'S THAT?

ハ゜タ〜ン…

BWA HA HA!

EXCELLENT, GENIE!

WITH YOUR POWERS, WE CAN RULE THE WORLD TOGETHER!

GIMME A BREAK, *MASTER.*

JAFAR, ARE YOU THINKING OF SETTING OUT ON YOUR OWN?

!!

...!

GENIE!

PLEASE SAVE JASMINE!

...!

WHERE DID YOU TAKE HER?!

AL...

TOO BAD. *I'M* GENIE'S MASTER NOW.

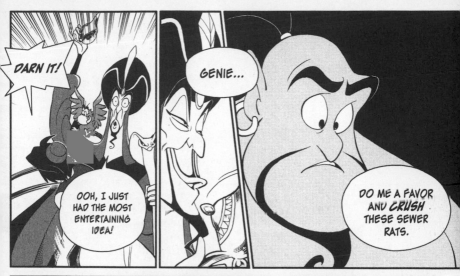

DARN IT!

OOH, I JUST HAD THE MOST ENTERTAINING IDEA!

GENIE...

DO ME A FAVOR AND *CRUSH* THESE SEWER RATS.

......

THAT'S A STUPID WISH!

DON'T LISTEN TO HIM, GENIE!

YOU HEARD ME. I COMMAND YOU TO TEACH THEM WHAT *PAIN* IS.

SORRY, AL.

GENIE, NO!

THE ONE WITH THE LAMP CALLS THE SHOTS...

Episode 23
Final Prayer

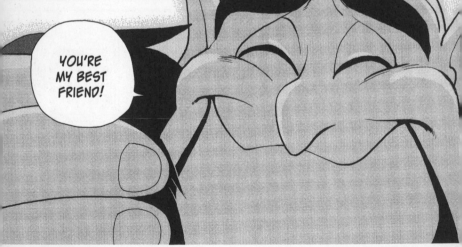

WE'LL FIND JASMINE.

SO HOLD ON TIGHT!

I BROKE FREE FROM THE LAMP'S SPELL...

...BUT YOU CAN RUB THIS LAMP ANYTIME YOU NEED MY HELP.

HERE, TAKE THIS.

I WANT TO HELP YOU RESCUE MY BEST FRIEND'S GIRLFRIEND!

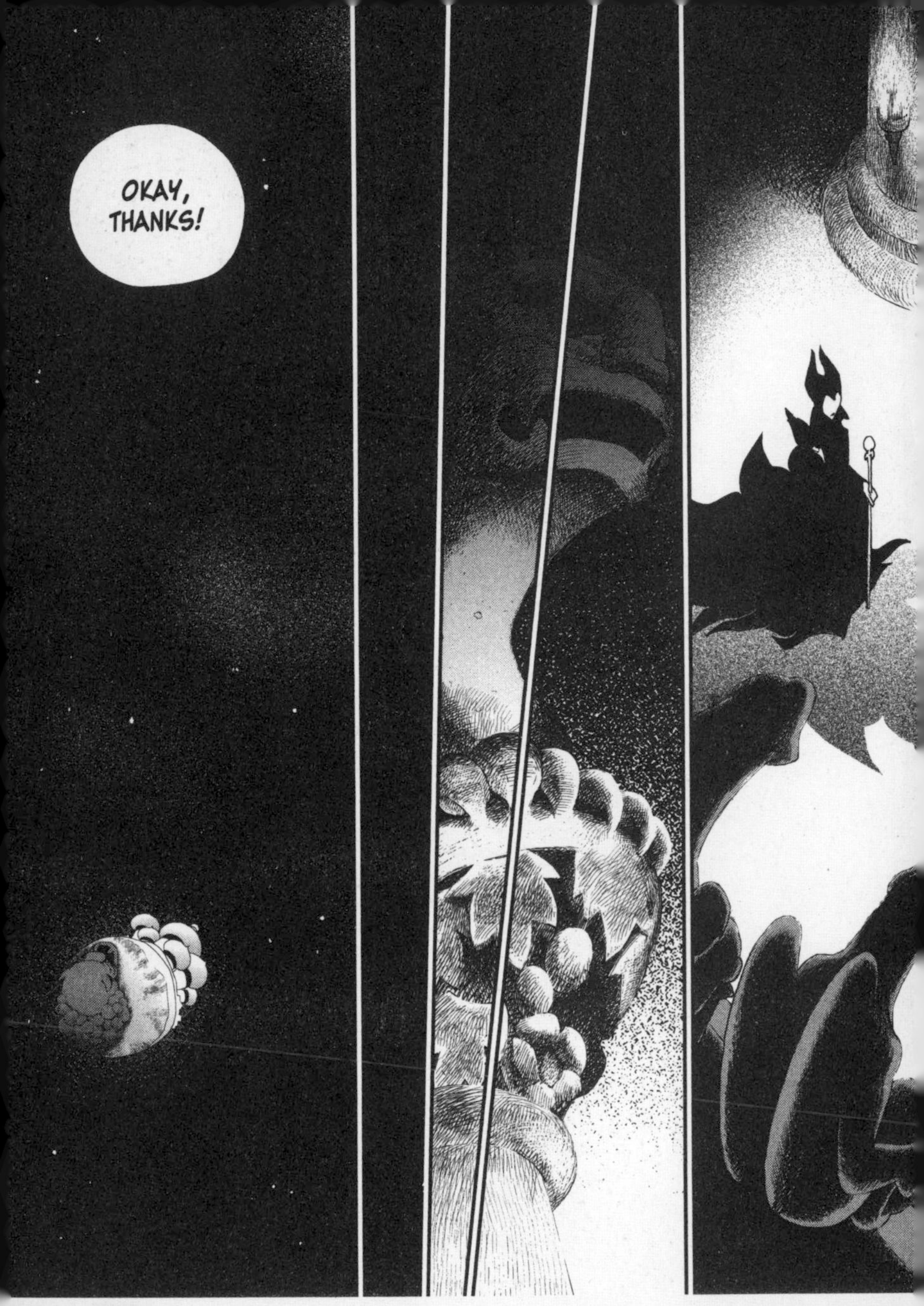
OKAY, THANKS!

Episode 24
Olympus Coliseum

YOU'RE PAYING SO MUCH ATTENTION TO THAT BOY.

HADES...

WHAT ARE YOU TRYING TO MAKE THE KID DO?

I HOPE YOU'RE NOT *HIDING* ANYTHING FROM US.

TRYING TO IGNORE ME?

OH WELL...

I GUESS IT WORKS BOTH WAYS.

I'LL JUST DO WHAT I HAVE TO DO.

CID?!

HOW DID YOU DO THIS?

Heh heh heh!

I installed it during the repair.

Didn't Chip 'n' Dale tell you?

YOU DIDN'T ASK MY PERMISS-ION!!!

Say what?

SORRY, DONALD'S A LITTLE EDGY RIGHT NOW.

We sealed Agrabah's Keyhole...

...and found a sheet from Ansem's report.

GOOD JOB, GENTLEMEN!

BUT I CAN'T READ WHAT'S WRITTEN IN THE REPORT.

Okay, fax it to me.

I'll do the decoding.

FAX?!

Pretty convenient, huh?

LEON'S GROUP IS ALSO GATHERING INFORMATION.

IT SEEMS THAT MALEFICENT IS UP TO SOMETHING...

WOW...

LOOK AT THAT HUGE GATE!

AHEM... LET'S SEE...

"HERE AT OLYMPUS COLISEUM..."

IT SAYS THEY PERIODICALLY HOLD A FIGHTING TOURNAMENT AT THE COLISEUM.

A FIGHTING TOURNAMENT?!!

?!

WE HAVE NO TIME FOR ANY TOURNAMENT!

SORA!

AWW, COME ON--LET'S JUST TAKE A PEEK!

INFORMATION

RULES

GOOD TIMING. GIVE ME A HAND, WILL YA?

EXCUSE ME...

MOVE THAT PEDESTAL OVER THERE FOR ME.

WHAT?

WELL, OKAY... I GUESS.

NOW YOU'RE HELPING WITH HIS SPRING CLEANING!

A-HYUCK, A-HYUCK!

BE QUIET, WILL YOU?

I JUST HAVE TO MOVE THIS OVER...

...THERE!!

ARGH...

GRRRRRAAH!!

IT'S WAY TOO HEAVY!

WHAT? TOO HEAVY?

HERCULES! SINCE WHEN HAVE YOU BEEN SUCH A LITTLE--

OH. WRONG GUY. WHAT'RE *YOU* DOING HERE?

UMM... I WANT TO ENTER THE FIGHTING TOURNAMENT.

SORA!!

WHAT?

A PIP-SQUEAK LIKE YOU?

SOME KID WHO CAN'T EVEN MOVE A PEDESTAL?!

......

LISTEN UP! THIS HERE'S THE WORLD-FAMOUS COLISEUM!

HEROES ONLY!

IF YOU'RE QUALIFIED TO PARTICIPATE...

...THEN BRING AN ENTRY PASS!

BUT IF YOU CAN'T EVEN MOVE A PEDESTAL LIKE THIS...

URGH...

ARGH...

......

ANYHOW, I'M BUSY! SO RUN ALONG, PIP-SQUEAKS!

WHAT'S THAT OLD GOAT'S DEAL?!

TREATING ME LIKE A CHILD?!

YEAH! YOU'VE GOT HEROES STANDING RIGHT IN FRONT OF YOU.

HERE'S A REAL HERO CHOSEN BY THE KEYBLADE!

THAT'S RIGHT!

A-HYUCK!

YOU TELL 'EM, DONALD!

RATHER A STUBBORN OLD GOAT, WOULDN'T YOU SAY?

IGNORING A YOUNG CHALLENGER LIKE YOU.

245

CERTAINLY, HERCULES *IS* A PRIZE PUPIL.

BUT WHAT'S HE GOING TO DO WHEN HERCULES IS GONE?

WELL, NEVER MIND.

......

AND WHO ARE YOU?

WHOA, HOLD ON THERE, FUZZ BOY. WAIT, LET ME GUESS. YOU WANT TO ENTER THE GAMES, RIGHT?

YOU HAVE THE EYES OF A TRUE HERO!

WELL, THEN. GET A LOAD OF *THIS.*

A PASS?

CAN I REALLY HAVE THIS?

WHAT?!!

NO WAY... HOW DID YOU GET AHOLD OF THIS PASS?

I CAN ENTER THE TOURNAMENT WITH THIS, RIGHT?

MMMPH...

OH, ALL RIGHT.

...BUT...

WELL, LET'S SEE WHAT YOU CAN DO! THIS TRIAL IS TOUGH!

YOU GOT WHAT IT TAKES?!

W-WHAT?

HOW CONVENIENT THAT THE KID WITH THE KEYBLADE IS HERE.

HE'LL BE ENTERING THE TOURNAMENT. DON'T BLOW IT.

SORRY, BUT MY CONTRACT SAYS--

BUT TO GET TO HIM, YOU'VE GOTTA FIGHT THAT KID.

AND A FEW CASUALTIES HERE AND THERE-- SO MUCH THE BETTER, EH?

HADES, THE GREAT GOD OF THE UNDERWORLD, SWEATING OVER SOME KID?

I KNOW, I KNOW! IT SAYS...

...YOU'RE ONLY REQUIRED TO TAKE OUT HERCULES...

...IN THIS TOURNAMENT.

JEEZ.

STIFFER THAN THE STIFFS BACK HOME.

STILL...

...SUCKERS LIKE HIM ARE HARD TO COME BY.

RELAX SHOULDERS, CHIN TO YOUR CHEST!

WHY ARE THERE THUMBTACKS IN MY SHOES?!

Episode 25

That's What a Hero's All About

HER-
CULES!

HEY,
PHIL.

I'M DONE
CLEANING
THE
COLISEUM
TOILETS.

LET ME
INTRODUCE
YOU TO...

...THE MAN
WHO'S THE MOST
POPULAR HERO
AROUND HERE!

HERCULES!

...CLEANING
TOILETS?!

YEAH.

THAT'S WHAT YOU
ASKED ME TO DO.

BWA HA HA HA!
I CAN'T BELIEVE
I MADE A *HERO*
CLEAN *TOILETS*.

I ALSO
CHECKED
OVER THE
ENTRY LIST.

THERE SEEMS TO
BE A LARGE NUMBER
OF STRANGE FIRST-
TIMERS.

I WONDER WHERE
THEY GOT THEIR
TICKETS.

THE STRONGEST, KINDEST AND MOST HANDSOME HERO...

HERCULES.

HE'S THE ONLY THING STANDING BETWEEN ME AND WORLD DOMINATION!

BUT WHY WORRY?

AHH!

NOW ALL THE PIECES ARE IN PLACE.

THAT BOY WILL TAKE OUT BOTH THE KID WITH THE KEYBLADE *AND* HERCULES.

ONCE I GET RID OF HERCULES, THE REST IS EASY.

GRAH!

GOOD JOB, KID!

DO IT!

Winner-- Team Sora!

HIYAH!

ALL RIGHT, WE'RE WINNING OUR WAY UP THE LADDER!

LET'S KEEP THIS STREAK GOING!

WAITING ROOM

?

WHAT'S THE MATTER?

CAN HE TAKE THEM ON ALONE?

HERCULES!

THIS AIN'T JUST SOME MATCH. THIS IS FOR REAL!

!

WHERE ARE YOU GOING, KID?

I'M GOING TO HELP HERCULES.

WHAT?!

I KNOW! I'M NOT AFRAID.

YOU CAN DECIDE IF I'M HERO MATERIAL OR NOT.

SORA, HOW COME YOU ALWAYS HAVE TO BE THE GOOD GUY?

!

WE'RE GOING WITH YOU!

A-HYUCK!

KINGDOM HEARTS
FOUR-PANEL
COMIC STRIPS

Come On Out, Genie!

LET ME KNOW IF YOU NEED ANYTHING!

MAGIC LAMP

THANKS!

COME ON OUT, GENIE...

THE MASTER IS CALLING!

CAN YOU OPEN THIS JAR FOR ME?

Café du Aerith

LEON, HAVE SOME LEMONADE.

NO THANKS.

YOU NEVER DRINK MY LEMONADE...

IT'S REALLY GOOD, LEON!

. . . .

I WOULD DRINK IT...

THANKS...

...IF ONLY AERITH WOULD STOP PUTTING SALT IN IT...

A Day in the Life of Cid

MORNING

15

NOON

15

EVENING

15

AH, MAN! I ACCIDENTALLY SLEPT FOR 18 HOURS!!!

A Day in the Life of Cid
—END

Final Mix Juice

LEON, ARE YOU THIRSTY?

WAIT, I DON'T WANT ANY MORE LEMONADE.

I KNOW-- THAT'S WHY I BROUGHT YOU A SODA.

SODA? ALL RIGHT, I'LL HAVE SOME.

GREAT!

....

WHAT...ON... EARTH?

DON'T YOU KNOW SODA TASTES GREAT WITH MILK?

NO, IT DOESN'T!!!

Mr. Fancy

DARN HERCULES...

I CAN'T BELIEVE HE'S SELLING HIS OWN TOY!

KIDS MUST BUY THIS AND SAY SOMETHING LIKE, "YEAH! HERCULES RULES!"

I'VE HAD ENOUGH!

I'LL SHOW YOU WHO'S BOSS!!

DISNEY · SQUARESOFT

KINGDOM HEARTS